THIS BOOK BELONGS TO:

CONTACT INFORMATION	
NAME	
ADDRESS	
PHONE #	
EMAIL	

DEDICATION

This Firearms Log Book is dedicated to gun owners and firearm enthusiasts who want to track and record their gun collection and ammunition inventory.

You are my inspiration for producing this book and I'm honored to be a part of your record-keeping and organization.

HOW TO USE THIS BOOK

This Firearms Log Book will help you by accurately planning, recording, and organizing your information.

Here are examples of information for you to fill in and write the details of your logbook.

Fill in the following information:

1. Master Index - record gun, serial number, brand/model, purchase date

2. Insurance Details - record company, policy #, start/end date, price, coverage type, contact #, email, fax, and website

3. Information - record brand, model, action, gauge/caliber, barrel, sights, stocks/grips, serial #, condition, unique marks, acquisition date, cost, appraised value, where the gun was acquired, comments, history, notes, repairs, date, cost, sold to, date, price, selling cost, a place for a photo

4. Acquisition Information - record purchased from, address, contact number, date, the price paid, ID #, DOB, condition, and comments

5. Deposition Information - record transfer/sold to, address, contact information, FOID/FFL#, date, the price paid, ID#, DOB, lost/stolen, incident #, details, condition, signature, gun owner transfer upon death, space for notes

MASTER INDEX

GUN	SERIAL NUMBER	BRAND/MODEL	DATE PURCHASED

MASTER INDEX

GUN	SERIAL NUMBER	BRAND/MODEL	DATE PURCHASED

MASTER INDEX

GUN	SERIAL NUMBER	BRAND/MODEL	DATE PURCHASED

INSURANCE DETAILS

COMPANY	
POLICY NUMBER	
START DATE	END DATE
PRICE	
COVERAGE TYPE	
CONTACT NUMBER	
EMAIL	
FAX	
WEBSITE	

COMPANY	
POLICY NUMBER	
START DATE	END DATE
PRICE	
COVERAGE TYPE	
CONTACT NUMBER	
EMAIL	
FAX	
WEBSITE	

COMPANY	
POLICY NUMBER	
START DATE	END DATE
PRICE	
COVERAGE TYPE	
CONTACT NUMBER	
EMAIL	
FAX	
WEBSITE	

COMPANY	
POLICY NUMBER	
START DATE	END DATE
PRICE	
COVERAGE TYPE	
CONTACT NUMBER	
EMAIL	
FAX	
WEBSITE	

INSURANCE DETAILS

COMPANY	
POLICY NUMBER	
START DATE	END DATE
PRICE	
COVERAGE TYPE	
CONTACT NUMBER	
EMAIL	
FAX	
WEBSITE	

COMPANY	
POLICY NUMBER	
START DATE	END DATE
PRICE	
COVERAGE TYPE	
CONTACT NUMBER	
EMAIL	
FAX	
WEBSITE	

COMPANY	
POLICY NUMBER	
START DATE	END DATE
PRICE	
COVERAGE TYPE	
CONTACT NUMBER	
EMAIL	
FAX	
WEBSITE	

COMPANY	
POLICY NUMBER	
START DATE	END DATE
PRICE	
COVERAGE TYPE	
CONTACT NUMBER	
EMAIL	
FAX	
WEBSITE	

INSURANCE DETAILS

COMPANY	
POLICY NUMBER	
START DATE	END DATE
PRICE	
COVERAGE TYPE	
CONTACT NUMBER	
EMAIL	
FAX	
WEBSITE	

COMPANY	
POLICY NUMBER	
START DATE	END DATE
PRICE	
COVERAGE TYPE	
CONTACT NUMBER	
EMAIL	
FAX	
WEBSITE	

COMPANY	
POLICY NUMBER	
START DATE	END DATE
PRICE	
COVERAGE TYPE	
CONTACT NUMBER	
EMAIL	
FAX	
WEBSITE	

COMPANY	
POLICY NUMBER	
START DATE	END DATE
PRICE	
COVERAGE TYPE	
CONTACT NUMBER	
EMAIL	
FAX	
WEBSITE	

INSURANCE DETAILS

COMPANY	
POLICY NUMBER	
START DATE	END DATE
PRICE	
COVERAGE TYPE	
CONTACT NUMBER	
EMAIL	
FAX	
WEBSITE	

COMPANY	
POLICY NUMBER	
START DATE	END DATE
PRICE	
COVERAGE TYPE	
CONTACT NUMBER	
EMAIL	
FAX	
WEBSITE	

COMPANY	
POLICY NUMBER	
START DATE	END DATE
PRICE	
COVERAGE TYPE	
CONTACT NUMBER	
EMAIL	
FAX	
WEBSITE	

COMPANY	
POLICY NUMBER	
START DATE	END DATE
PRICE	
COVERAGE TYPE	
CONTACT NUMBER	
EMAIL	
FAX	
WEBSITE	

INSURANCE DETAILS

COMPANY	
POLICY NUMBER	
START DATE	END DATE
PRICE	
COVERAGE TYPE	
CONTACT NUMBER	
EMAIL	
FAX	
WEBSITE	

COMPANY	
POLICY NUMBER	
START DATE	END DATE
PRICE	
COVERAGE TYPE	
CONTACT NUMBER	
EMAIL	
FAX	
WEBSITE	

COMPANY	
POLICY NUMBER	
START DATE	END DATE
PRICE	
COVERAGE TYPE	
CONTACT NUMBER	
EMAIL	
FAX	
WEBSITE	

COMPANY	
POLICY NUMBER	
START DATE	END DATE
PRICE	
COVERAGE TYPE	
CONTACT NUMBER	
EMAIL	
FAX	
WEBSITE	

INFORMATION

BRAND		MODEL	
ACTION		GAUGE OR CALIBER	
BARREL		SIGHTS	
STOCKS OR GRIPS			
SERIAL #		CONDITION	
UNIQUE MARKS			

ACQUISITION DATE		COST		APPRAISED VALUE	

WHERE ACQUIRED	
COMMENTS	
HISTORY	
NOTES	

REPAIRS	DATE	COST

SOLD TO		
DATE		SELLING PRICE

ACQUISITION INFORMATION

PURCHASED FROM	
ADDRESS	
CONTACT NUMBER	

DATE		PRICE PAID	
ID NUMBER		D.O.B.	

CONDITION	
COMMENTS	

DISPOSITION INFORMATION

TRANSFER / SOLD TO	
ADDRESS	
CONTACT NUMBER	
FOID OR FFL #	

DATE		PRICE PAID	
ID NUMBER		D.O.B.	
LOST / STOLEN		INCIDENT #	

DETAILS	
CONDITION	
SIGNATURE	

IN THE EVENT OF MY DEMISE I WANT THIS FIREARM TO GO TO	

NOTES

INFORMATION

BRAND		MODEL	
ACTION		GAUGE OR CALIBER	
BARREL		SIGHTS	
STOCKS OR GRIPS			
SERIAL #		CONDITION	
UNIQUE MARKS			

ACQUISITION DATE		COST		APPRAISED VALUE	

WHERE ACQUIRED	
COMMENTS	
HISTORY	
NOTES	

REPAIRS	DATE	COST

SOLD TO	
DATE		SELLING PRICE	

ACQUISITION INFORMATION

PURCHASED FROM	
ADDRESS	
CONTACT NUMBER	

DATE		PRICE PAID	
ID NUMBER		D.O.B.	

CONDITION	
COMMENTS	

DISPOSITION INFORMATION

TRANSFER / SOLD TO	
ADDRESS	
CONTACT NUMBER	
FOID OR FFL #	

DATE		PRICE PAID	
ID NUMBER		D.O.B.	
LOST / STOLEN		INCIDENT #	

DETAILS	
CONDITION	
SIGNATURE	

IN THE EVENT OF MY DEMISE I WANT THIS FIREARM TO GO TO	

NOTES

INFORMATION

BRAND		MODEL	
ACTION		GAUGE OR CALIBER	
BARREL		SIGHTS	
STOCKS OR GRIPS			
SERIAL #		CONDITION	
UNIQUE MARKS			

ACQUISITION DATE		COST		APPRAISED VALUE	

WHERE ACQUIRED	
COMMENTS	
HISTORY	
NOTES	

REPAIRS	DATE	COST

SOLD TO		
DATE		SELLING PRICE

ACQUISITION INFORMATION

PURCHASED FROM	
ADDRESS	
CONTACT NUMBER	
DATE	PRICE PAID
ID NUMBER	D.O.B.
CONDITION	
COMMENTS	

DISPOSITION INFORMATION

TRANSFER / SOLD TO	
ADDRESS	
CONTACT NUMBER	
FOID OR FFL #	
DATE	PRICE PAID
ID NUMBER	D.O.B.
LOST / STOLEN	INCIDENT #
DETAILS	
CONDITION	
SIGNATURE	

IN THE EVENT OF MY DEMISE I WANT THIS FIREARM TO GO TO	

NOTES

INFORMATION

BRAND		MODEL	
ACTION		GAUGE OR CALIBER	
BARREL		SIGHTS	
STOCKS OR GRIPS			
SERIAL #		CONDITION	
UNIQUE MARKS			
ACQUISITION DATE		COST	APPRAISED VALUE
WHERE ACQUIRED			
COMMENTS			
HISTORY			
NOTES			

REPAIRS	DATE	COST

SOLD TO			
DATE		SELLING PRICE	

ACQUISITION INFORMATION

PURCHASED FROM	
ADDRESS	
CONTACT NUMBER	
DATE	
ID NUMBER	
CONDITION	
COMMENTS	

PRICE PAID	
D.O.B.	

DISPOSITION INFORMATION

TRANSFER / SOLD TO	
ADDRESS	
CONTACT NUMBER	
FOID OR FFL #	
DATE	
ID NUMBER	
LOST / STOLEN	
DETAILS	
CONDITION	
SIGNATURE	

PRICE PAID	
D.O.B.	
INCIDENT #	

IN THE EVENT OF MY DEMISE I WANT THIS FIREARM TO GO TO	

NOTES

INFORMATION

BRAND		MODEL	
ACTION		GAUGE OR CALIBER	
BARREL		SIGHTS	
STOCKS OR GRIPS			
SERIAL #		CONDITION	
UNIQUE MARKS			

ACQUISITION DATE		COST		APPRAISED VALUE	

WHERE ACQUIRED	
COMMENTS	
HISTORY	
NOTES	

REPAIRS	DATE	COST

SOLD TO		
DATE		SELLING PRICE

ACQUISITION INFORMATION

PURCHASED FROM	
ADDRESS	
CONTACT NUMBER	

DATE		PRICE PAID	
ID NUMBER		D.O.B.	

CONDITION	
COMMENTS	

DISPOSITION INFORMATION

TRANSFER / SOLD TO	
ADDRESS	
CONTACT NUMBER	
FOID OR FFL #	

DATE		PRICE PAID	
ID NUMBER		D.O.B.	
LOST / STOLEN		INCIDENT #	

DETAILS	
CONDITION	
SIGNATURE	

IN THE EVENT OF MY DEMISE I WANT THIS FIREARM TO GO TO	

NOTES

INFORMATION

BRAND		MODEL	
ACTION		GAUGE OR CALIBER	
BARREL		SIGHTS	
STOCKS OR GRIPS			
SERIAL #		CONDITION	
UNIQUE MARKS			

ACQUISITION DATE		COST		APPRAISED VALUE	

WHERE ACQUIRED	
COMMENTS	
HISTORY	
NOTES	

REPAIRS	DATE	COST

SOLD TO	
DATE	SELLING PRICE

ACQUISITION INFORMATION

PURCHASED FROM	
ADDRESS	
CONTACT NUMBER	

DATE		PRICE PAID	
ID NUMBER		D.O.B.	

CONDITION	
COMMENTS	

DISPOSITION INFORMATION

TRANSFER / SOLD TO	
ADDRESS	
CONTACT NUMBER	
FOID OR FFL #	

DATE		PRICE PAID	
ID NUMBER		D.O.B.	
LOST / STOLEN		INCIDENT #	

DETAILS	
CONDITION	
SIGNATURE	

IN THE EVENT OF MY DEMISE I WANT THIS FIREARM TO GO TO	

NOTES

INFORMATION

BRAND		MODEL	
ACTION		GAUGE OR CALIBER	
BARREL		SIGHTS	
STOCKS OR GRIPS			
SERIAL #		CONDITION	
UNIQUE MARKS			

ACQUISITION DATE		COST		APPRAISED VALUE	

WHERE ACQUIRED	
COMMENTS	
HISTORY	
NOTES	

REPAIRS	DATE	COST

SOLD TO			
DATE		SELLING PRICE	

ACQUISITION INFORMATION

PURCHASED FROM	
ADDRESS	
CONTACT NUMBER	
DATE	PRICE PAID
ID NUMBER	D.O.B.
CONDITION	
COMMENTS	

DISPOSITION INFORMATION

TRANSFER / SOLD TO		
ADDRESS		
CONTACT NUMBER		
FOID OR FFL #		
DATE	PRICE PAID	
ID NUMBER	D.O.B.	
LOST / STOLEN	INCIDENT #	
DETAILS		
CONDITION		
SIGNATURE		

IN THE EVENT OF MY DEMISE I WANT THIS FIREARM TO GO TO	

NOTES

INFORMATION

BRAND		MODEL	
ACTION		GAUGE OR CALIBER	
BARREL		SIGHTS	
STOCKS OR GRIPS			
SERIAL #		CONDITION	
UNIQUE MARKS			

ACQUISITION DATE		COST		APPRAISED VALUE	
WHERE ACQUIRED					
COMMENTS					
HISTORY					
NOTES					

REPAIRS	DATE	COST

SOLD TO	
DATE		SELLING PRICE	

ACQUISITION INFORMATION

PURCHASED FROM	
ADDRESS	
CONTACT NUMBER	
DATE	PRICE PAID
ID NUMBER	D.O.B.
CONDITION	
COMMENTS	

DISPOSITION INFORMATION

TRANSFER / SOLD TO	
ADDRESS	
CONTACT NUMBER	
FOID OR FFL #	
DATE	PRICE PAID
ID NUMBER	D.O.B.
LOST / STOLEN	INCIDENT #
DETAILS	
CONDITION	
SIGNATURE	

IN THE EVENT OF MY DEMISE I WANT THIS FIREARM TO GO TO	

NOTES

INFORMATION

BRAND		MODEL	
ACTION		GAUGE OR CALIBER	
BARREL		SIGHTS	
STOCKS OR GRIPS			
SERIAL #		CONDITION	
UNIQUE MARKS			

ACQUISITION DATE		COST		APPRAISED VALUE	

WHERE ACQUIRED	
COMMENTS	
HISTORY	
NOTES	

REPAIRS	DATE	COST

SOLD TO			
DATE		SELLING PRICE	

ACQUISITION INFORMATION

PURCHASED FROM	
ADDRESS	
CONTACT NUMBER	

DATE		PRICE PAID	
ID NUMBER		D.O.B.	

CONDITION	
COMMENTS	

DISPOSITION INFORMATION

TRANSFER / SOLD TO	
ADDRESS	
CONTACT NUMBER	
FOID OR FFL #	

DATE		PRICE PAID	
ID NUMBER		D.O.B.	
LOST / STOLEN		INCIDENT #	

DETAILS	
CONDITION	
SIGNATURE	

IN THE EVENT OF MY DEMISE I WANT THIS FIREARM TO GO TO	

NOTES

INFORMATION

BRAND		MODEL	
ACTION		GAUGE OR CALIBER	
BARREL		SIGHTS	
STOCKS OR GRIPS			
SERIAL #		CONDITION	
UNIQUE MARKS			

ACQUISITION DATE		COST		APPRAISED VALUE	
WHERE ACQUIRED					
COMMENTS					
HISTORY					
NOTES					

REPAIRS	DATE	COST

SOLD TO			
DATE		SELLING PRICE	

ACQUISITION INFORMATION

PURCHASED FROM	
ADDRESS	
CONTACT NUMBER	
DATE	PRICE PAID
ID NUMBER	D.O.B.
CONDITION	
COMMENTS	

DISPOSITION INFORMATION

TRANSFER / SOLD TO	
ADDRESS	
CONTACT NUMBER	
FOID OR FFL #	
DATE	PRICE PAID
ID NUMBER	D.O.B.
LOST / STOLEN	INCIDENT #
DETAILS	
CONDITION	
SIGNATURE	

IN THE EVENT OF MY DEMISE I WANT THIS FIREARM TO GO TO	

NOTES

INFORMATION

BRAND		MODEL	
ACTION		GAUGE OR CALIBER	
BARREL		SIGHTS	
STOCKS OR GRIPS			
SERIAL #		CONDITION	
UNIQUE MARKS			

ACQUISITION DATE		COST		APPRAISED VALUE

WHERE ACQUIRED	
COMMENTS	
HISTORY	
NOTES	

REPAIRS	DATE	COST

SOLD TO			
DATE		SELLING PRICE	

ACQUISITION INFORMATION

PURCHASED FROM	
ADDRESS	
CONTACT NUMBER	
DATE	PRICE PAID
ID NUMBER	D.O.B.
CONDITION	
COMMENTS	

DISPOSITION INFORMATION

TRANSFER / SOLD TO		
ADDRESS		
CONTACT NUMBER		
FOID OR FFL #		
DATE	PRICE PAID	
ID NUMBER	D.O.B.	
LOST / STOLEN	INCIDENT #	
DETAILS		
CONDITION		
SIGNATURE		

IN THE EVENT OF MY DEMISE I WANT THIS FIREARM TO GO TO	

NOTES

INFORMATION

BRAND		MODEL	
ACTION		GAUGE OR CALIBER	
BARREL		SIGHTS	
STOCKS OR GRIPS			
SERIAL #		CONDITION	
UNIQUE MARKS			

ACQUISITION DATE		COST		APPRAISED VALUE	

WHERE ACQUIRED	
COMMENTS	
HISTORY	
NOTES	

REPAIRS	DATE	COST

SOLD TO			
DATE		SELLING PRICE	

ACQUISITION INFORMATION

PURCHASED FROM	
ADDRESS	
CONTACT NUMBER	

DATE		PRICE PAID	
ID NUMBER		D.O.B.	

CONDITION	
COMMENTS	

DISPOSITION INFORMATION

TRANSFER / SOLD TO	
ADDRESS	
CONTACT NUMBER	
FOID OR FFL #	

DATE		PRICE PAID	
ID NUMBER		D.O.B.	
LOST / STOLEN		INCIDENT #	

DETAILS	
CONDITION	
SIGNATURE	

IN THE EVENT OF MY DEMISE I WANT THIS FIREARM TO GO TO	

NOTES

INFORMATION

BRAND		MODEL	
ACTION		GAUGE OR CALIBER	
BARREL		SIGHTS	
STOCKS OR GRIPS			
SERIAL #		CONDITION	
UNIQUE MARKS			
ACQUISITION DATE		COST	APPRAISED VALUE
WHERE ACQUIRED			
COMMENTS			
HISTORY			
NOTES			

REPAIRS	DATE	COST

SOLD TO			
DATE		SELLING PRICE	

ACQUISITION INFORMATION

PURCHASED FROM	
ADDRESS	
CONTACT NUMBER	

DATE		PRICE PAID	
ID NUMBER		D.O.B.	

CONDITION	
COMMENTS	

DISPOSITION INFORMATION

TRANSFER / SOLD TO	
ADDRESS	
CONTACT NUMBER	
FOID OR FFL #	

DATE		PRICE PAID	
ID NUMBER		D.O.B.	
LOST / STOLEN		INCIDENT #	

DETAILS	
CONDITION	
SIGNATURE	

IN THE EVENT OF MY DEMISE I WANT THIS FIREARM TO GO TO	

NOTES

INFORMATION

BRAND		MODEL	
ACTION		GAUGE OR CALIBER	
BARREL		SIGHTS	
STOCKS OR GRIPS			
SERIAL #		CONDITION	
UNIQUE MARKS			

ACQUISITION DATE		COST		APPRAISED VALUE	
WHERE ACQUIRED					
COMMENTS					
HISTORY					
NOTES					

	REPAIRS	DATE	COST

SOLD TO			
DATE		SELLING PRICE	

ACQUISITION INFORMATION

PURCHASED FROM	
ADDRESS	
CONTACT NUMBER	
DATE	PRICE PAID
ID NUMBER	D.O.B.
CONDITION	
COMMENTS	

DISPOSITION INFORMATION

TRANSFER / SOLD TO		
ADDRESS		
CONTACT NUMBER		
FOID OR FFL #		
DATE	PRICE PAID	
ID NUMBER	D.O.B.	
LOST / STOLEN	INCIDENT #	
DETAILS		
CONDITION		
SIGNATURE		

IN THE EVENT OF MY DEMISE I WANT THIS FIREARM TO GO TO	

NOTES

INFORMATION

BRAND		MODEL	
ACTION		GAUGE OR CALIBER	
BARREL		SIGHTS	
STOCKS OR GRIPS			
SERIAL #		CONDITION	
UNIQUE MARKS			

ACQUISITION DATE		COST		APPRAISED VALUE	
WHERE ACQUIRED					
COMMENTS					
HISTORY					
NOTES					

REPAIRS	DATE	COST

SOLD TO			
DATE		SELLING PRICE	

ACQUISITION INFORMATION

PURCHASED FROM	
ADDRESS	
CONTACT NUMBER	
DATE		PRICE PAID	
ID NUMBER		D.O.B.	
CONDITION	
COMMENTS	

DISPOSITION INFORMATION

TRANSFER / SOLD TO	
ADDRESS	
CONTACT NUMBER	
FOID OR FFL #	
DATE		PRICE PAID	
ID NUMBER		D.O.B.	
LOST / STOLEN		INCIDENT #	
DETAILS	
CONDITION	
SIGNATURE	

IN THE EVENT OF MY DEMISE I WANT THIS FIREARM TO GO TO	

NOTES

INFORMATION

BRAND		MODEL	
ACTION		GAUGE OR CALIBER	
BARREL		SIGHTS	
STOCKS OR GRIPS			
SERIAL #		CONDITION	
UNIQUE MARKS			
ACQUISITION DATE		COST	APPRAISED VALUE
WHERE ACQUIRED			
COMMENTS			
HISTORY			
NOTES			

REPAIRS	DATE	COST

SOLD TO			
DATE		SELLING PRICE	

ACQUISITION INFORMATION

PURCHASED FROM	
ADDRESS	
CONTACT NUMBER	
DATE	PRICE PAID
ID NUMBER	D.O.B.
CONDITION	
COMMENTS	

DISPOSITION INFORMATION

TRANSFER / SOLD TO	
ADDRESS	
CONTACT NUMBER	
FOID OR FFL #	
DATE	PRICE PAID
ID NUMBER	D.O.B.
LOST / STOLEN	INCIDENT #
DETAILS	
CONDITION	
SIGNATURE	

IN THE EVENT OF MY DEMISE I WANT THIS FIREARM TO GO TO	

NOTES

INFORMATION

BRAND		MODEL	
ACTION		GAUGE OR CALIBER	
BARREL		SIGHTS	
STOCKS OR GRIPS			
SERIAL #		CONDITION	
UNIQUE MARKS			
ACQUISITION DATE		COST	APPRAISED VALUE
WHERE ACQUIRED			
COMMENTS			
HISTORY			
NOTES			

REPAIRS	DATE	COST

SOLD TO	
DATE	SELLING PRICE

ACQUISITION INFORMATION

PURCHASED FROM	
ADDRESS	
CONTACT NUMBER	
DATE	PRICE PAID
ID NUMBER	D.O.B.
CONDITION	
COMMENTS	

DISPOSITION INFORMATION

TRANSFER / SOLD TO	
ADDRESS	
CONTACT NUMBER	
FOID OR FFL #	
DATE	PRICE PAID
ID NUMBER	D.O.B.
LOST / STOLEN	INCIDENT #
DETAILS	
CONDITION	
SIGNATURE	

IN THE EVENT OF MY DEMISE I WANT THIS FIREARM TO GO TO	

NOTES

INFORMATION

BRAND		MODEL	
ACTION		GAUGE OR CALIBER	
BARREL		SIGHTS	
STOCKS OR GRIPS			
SERIAL #		CONDITION	
UNIQUE MARKS			

ACQUISITION DATE		COST		APPRAISED VALUE	

WHERE ACQUIRED	
COMMENTS	
HISTORY	
NOTES	

REPAIRS	DATE	COST

SOLD TO	
DATE		SELLING PRICE	

ACQUISITION INFORMATION

PURCHASED FROM	
ADDRESS	
CONTACT NUMBER	
DATE		PRICE PAID	
ID NUMBER		D.O.B.	
CONDITION	
COMMENTS	

DISPOSITION INFORMATION

TRANSFER / SOLD TO	
ADDRESS	
CONTACT NUMBER	
FOID OR FFL #	
DATE		PRICE PAID	
ID NUMBER		D.O.B.	
LOST / STOLEN		INCIDENT #	
DETAILS	
CONDITION	
SIGNATURE	

IN THE EVENT OF MY DEMISE I WANT THIS FIREARM TO GO TO	

NOTES

INFORMATION

BRAND		MODEL	
ACTION		GAUGE OR CALIBER	
BARREL		SIGHTS	
STOCKS OR GRIPS			
SERIAL #		CONDITION	
UNIQUE MARKS			

ACQUISITION DATE		COST		APPRAISED VALUE	

WHERE ACQUIRED	
COMMENTS	
HISTORY	
NOTES	

REPAIRS	DATE	COST

SOLD TO		
DATE	SELLING PRICE	

ACQUISITION INFORMATION

PURCHASED FROM	
ADDRESS	
CONTACT NUMBER	
DATE	
ID NUMBER	
CONDITION	
COMMENTS	

DATE		PRICE PAID	
ID NUMBER		D.O.B.	

DISPOSITION INFORMATION

TRANSFER / SOLD TO	
ADDRESS	
CONTACT NUMBER	
FOID OR FFL #	
DATE	
ID NUMBER	
LOST / STOLEN	
DETAILS	
CONDITION	
SIGNATURE	

DATE		PRICE PAID	
ID NUMBER		D.O.B.	
LOST / STOLEN		INCIDENT #	

IN THE EVENT OF MY DEMISE I WANT THIS FIREARM TO GO TO	

NOTES

INFORMATION

BRAND		MODEL	
ACTION		GAUGE OR CALIBER	
BARREL		SIGHTS	
STOCKS OR GRIPS			
SERIAL #		CONDITION	
UNIQUE MARKS			

ACQUISITION DATE		COST		APPRAISED VALUE	

WHERE ACQUIRED	
COMMENTS	
HISTORY	
NOTES	

REPAIRS	DATE	COST

SOLD TO			
DATE		SELLING PRICE	

ACQUISITION INFORMATION

PURCHASED FROM	
ADDRESS	
CONTACT NUMBER	
DATE		PRICE PAID	
ID NUMBER		D.O.B.	
CONDITION	
COMMENTS	

DISPOSITION INFORMATION

TRANSFER / SOLD TO	
ADDRESS	
CONTACT NUMBER	
FOID OR FFL #	
DATE		PRICE PAID	
ID NUMBER		D.O.B.	
LOST / STOLEN		INCIDENT #	
DETAILS	
CONDITION	
SIGNATURE	

IN THE EVENT OF MY DEMISE I WANT THIS FIREARM TO GO TO	

NOTES

INFORMATION

BRAND		MODEL	
ACTION		GAUGE OR CALIBER	
BARREL		SIGHTS	
STOCKS OR GRIPS			
SERIAL #		CONDITION	
UNIQUE MARKS			

ACQUISITION DATE		COST		APPRAISED VALUE	

WHERE ACQUIRED	
COMMENTS	
HISTORY	
NOTES	

REPAIRS	DATE	COST

SOLD TO			
DATE		SELLING PRICE	

ACQUISITION INFORMATION

PURCHASED FROM	
ADDRESS	
CONTACT NUMBER	
DATE	
ID NUMBER	
CONDITION	
COMMENTS	

DATE		PRICE PAID	
ID NUMBER		D.O.B.	

DISPOSITION INFORMATION

TRANSFER / SOLD TO	
ADDRESS	
CONTACT NUMBER	
FOID OR FFL #	
DATE	
ID NUMBER	
LOST / STOLEN	
DETAILS	
CONDITION	
SIGNATURE	

DATE		PRICE PAID	
ID NUMBER		D.O.B.	
LOST / STOLEN		INCIDENT #	

IN THE EVENT OF MY DEMISE I WANT THIS FIREARM TO GO TO	

NOTES

INFORMATION

BRAND		MODEL	
ACTION		GAUGE OR CALIBER	
BARREL		SIGHTS	
STOCKS OR GRIPS			
SERIAL #		CONDITION	
UNIQUE MARKS			

ACQUISITION DATE		COST		APPRAISED VALUE	

WHERE ACQUIRED	
COMMENTS	
HISTORY	
NOTES	

REPAIRS	DATE	COST

SOLD TO			
DATE		SELLING PRICE	

ACQUISITION INFORMATION

PURCHASED FROM	
ADDRESS	
CONTACT NUMBER	
DATE		PRICE PAID	
ID NUMBER		D.O.B.	
CONDITION	
COMMENTS	

DISPOSITION INFORMATION

TRANSFER / SOLD TO	
ADDRESS	
CONTACT NUMBER	
FOID OR FFL #	
DATE		PRICE PAID	
ID NUMBER		D.O.B.	
LOST / STOLEN		INCIDENT #	
DETAILS	
CONDITION	
SIGNATURE	

IN THE EVENT OF MY DEMISE I WANT THIS FIREARM TO GO TO	

NOTES

INFORMATION

BRAND		MODEL	
ACTION		GAUGE OR CALIBER	
BARREL		SIGHTS	
STOCKS OR GRIPS			
SERIAL #		CONDITION	
UNIQUE MARKS			

ACQUISITION DATE		COST		APPRAISED VALUE	

WHERE ACQUIRED	
COMMENTS	
HISTORY	
NOTES	

REPAIRS	DATE	COST

SOLD TO			
DATE		SELLING PRICE	

ACQUISITION INFORMATION

PURCHASED FROM	
ADDRESS	
CONTACT NUMBER	

DATE		PRICE PAID	
ID NUMBER		D.O.B.	

CONDITION	
COMMENTS	

DISPOSITION INFORMATION

TRANSFER / SOLD TO	
ADDRESS	
CONTACT NUMBER	
FOID OR FFL #	

DATE		PRICE PAID	
ID NUMBER		D.O.B.	
LOST / STOLEN		INCIDENT #	

DETAILS	
CONDITION	
SIGNATURE	

IN THE EVENT OF MY DEMISE I WANT THIS FIREARM TO GO TO	

NOTES

INFORMATION

BRAND		MODEL	
ACTION		GAUGE OR CALIBER	
BARREL		SIGHTS	
STOCKS OR GRIPS			
SERIAL #		CONDITION	
UNIQUE MARKS			

ACQUISITION DATE		COST		APPRAISED VALUE	

WHERE ACQUIRED	
COMMENTS	
HISTORY	
NOTES	

REPAIRS	DATE	COST

SOLD TO			
DATE		SELLING PRICE	

ACQUISITION INFORMATION

PURCHASED FROM	
ADDRESS	
CONTACT NUMBER	
DATE	
ID NUMBER	
CONDITION	
COMMENTS	

DATE		PRICE PAID	
ID NUMBER		D.O.B.	

DISPOSITION INFORMATION

TRANSFER / SOLD TO	
ADDRESS	
CONTACT NUMBER	
FOID OR FFL #	
DATE	
ID NUMBER	
LOST / STOLEN	
DETAILS	
CONDITION	
SIGNATURE	

DATE		PRICE PAID	
ID NUMBER		D.O.B.	
LOST / STOLEN		INCIDENT #	

IN THE EVENT OF MY DEMISE I WANT THIS FIREARM TO GO TO	

NOTES

INFORMATION

BRAND		MODEL	
ACTION		GAUGE OR CALIBER	
BARREL		SIGHTS	
STOCKS OR GRIPS			
SERIAL #		CONDITION	
UNIQUE MARKS			
ACQUISITION DATE		COST	APPRAISED VALUE
WHERE ACQUIRED			
COMMENTS			
HISTORY			
NOTES			

REPAIRS	DATE	COST

SOLD TO			
DATE		SELLING PRICE	

ACQUISITION INFORMATION

PURCHASED FROM	
ADDRESS	
CONTACT NUMBER	
DATE	
ID NUMBER	
CONDITION	
COMMENTS	

		PRICE PAID	
		D.O.B.	

DISPOSITION INFORMATION

TRANSFER / SOLD TO	
ADDRESS	
CONTACT NUMBER	
FOID OR FFL #	
DATE	
ID NUMBER	
LOST / STOLEN	
DETAILS	
CONDITION	
SIGNATURE	

		PRICE PAID	
		D.O.B.	
		INCIDENT #	

IN THE EVENT OF MY DEMISE I WANT THIS FIREARM TO GO TO	

NOTES

INFORMATION

BRAND		MODEL	
ACTION		GAUGE OR CALIBER	
BARREL		SIGHTS	
STOCKS OR GRIPS			
SERIAL #		CONDITION	
UNIQUE MARKS			
ACQUISITION DATE		COST	APPRAISED VALUE
WHERE ACQUIRED			
COMMENTS			
HISTORY			
NOTES			

REPAIRS	DATE	COST

SOLD TO		
DATE		SELLING PRICE

ACQUISITION INFORMATION

PURCHASED FROM	
ADDRESS	
CONTACT NUMBER	
DATE	PRICE PAID
ID NUMBER	D.O.B.
CONDITION	
COMMENTS	

DISPOSITION INFORMATION

TRANSFER / SOLD TO	
ADDRESS	
CONTACT NUMBER	
FOID OR FFL #	
DATE	PRICE PAID
ID NUMBER	D.O.B.
LOST / STOLEN	INCIDENT #
DETAILS	
CONDITION	
SIGNATURE	

IN THE EVENT OF MY DEMISE I WANT THIS FIREARM TO GO TO	

NOTES

INFORMATION

BRAND		MODEL	
ACTION		GAUGE OR CALIBER	
BARREL		SIGHTS	
STOCKS OR GRIPS			
SERIAL #		CONDITION	
UNIQUE MARKS			

ACQUISITION DATE		COST		APPRAISED VALUE	

WHERE ACQUIRED	
COMMENTS	
HISTORY	
NOTES	

REPAIRS	DATE	COST

SOLD TO			
DATE		SELLING PRICE	

ACQUISITION INFORMATION

PURCHASED FROM	
ADDRESS	
CONTACT NUMBER	

DATE		PRICE PAID	
ID NUMBER		D.O.B.	

CONDITION	
COMMENTS	

DISPOSITION INFORMATION

TRANSFER / SOLD TO	
ADDRESS	
CONTACT NUMBER	
FOID OR FFL #	

DATE		PRICE PAID	
ID NUMBER		D.O.B.	
LOST / STOLEN		INCIDENT #	

DETAILS	
CONDITION	
SIGNATURE	

IN THE EVENT OF MY DEMISE I WANT THIS FIREARM TO GO TO	

NOTES

INFORMATION

BRAND		MODEL	
ACTION		GAUGE OR CALIBER	
BARREL		SIGHTS	
STOCKS OR GRIPS			
SERIAL #		CONDITION	
UNIQUE MARKS			

ACQUISITION DATE		COST		APPRAISED VALUE	

WHERE ACQUIRED	
COMMENTS	
HISTORY	
NOTES	

REPAIRS	DATE	COST

SOLD TO			
DATE		SELLING PRICE	

ACQUISITION INFORMATION

PURCHASED FROM	
ADDRESS	
CONTACT NUMBER	
DATE	PRICE PAID
ID NUMBER	D.O.B.
CONDITION	
COMMENTS	

DISPOSITION INFORMATION

TRANSFER / SOLD TO	
ADDRESS	
CONTACT NUMBER	
FOID OR FFL #	
DATE	PRICE PAID
ID NUMBER	D.O.B.
LOST / STOLEN	INCIDENT #
DETAILS	
CONDITION	
SIGNATURE	

IN THE EVENT OF MY DEMISE I WANT THIS FIREARM TO GO TO	

NOTES

INFORMATION

BRAND		MODEL	
ACTION		GAUGE OR CALIBER	
BARREL		SIGHTS	
STOCKS OR GRIPS			
SERIAL #		CONDITION	
UNIQUE MARKS			

ACQUISITION DATE		COST		APPRAISED VALUE

WHERE ACQUIRED	
COMMENTS	
HISTORY	
NOTES	

REPAIRS	DATE	COST

SOLD TO			
DATE		SELLING PRICE	

ACQUISITION INFORMATION

PURCHASED FROM	
ADDRESS	
CONTACT NUMBER	
DATE	
ID NUMBER	
CONDITION	
COMMENTS	

DATE		PRICE PAID	
ID NUMBER		D.O.B.	

DISPOSITION INFORMATION

TRANSFER / SOLD TO	
ADDRESS	
CONTACT NUMBER	
FOID OR FFL #	
DATE	
ID NUMBER	
LOST / STOLEN	
DETAILS	
CONDITION	
SIGNATURE	

DATE		PRICE PAID	
ID NUMBER		D.O.B.	
LOST / STOLEN		INCIDENT #	

IN THE EVENT OF MY DEMISE I WANT THIS FIREARM TO GO TO	

NOTES

INFORMATION

BRAND		MODEL	
ACTION		GAUGE OR CALIBER	
BARREL		SIGHTS	
STOCKS OR GRIPS			
SERIAL #		CONDITION	
UNIQUE MARKS			

ACQUISITION DATE		COST		APPRAISED VALUE	

WHERE ACQUIRED	
COMMENTS	
HISTORY	
NOTES	

REPAIRS	DATE	COST

SOLD TO			
DATE		SELLING PRICE	

ACQUISITION INFORMATION

PURCHASED FROM	
ADDRESS	
CONTACT NUMBER	
DATE	PRICE PAID
ID NUMBER	D.O.B.
CONDITION	
COMMENTS	

DISPOSITION INFORMATION

TRANSFER / SOLD TO	
ADDRESS	
CONTACT NUMBER	
FOID OR FFL #	
DATE	PRICE PAID
ID NUMBER	D.O.B.
LOST / STOLEN	INCIDENT #
DETAILS	
CONDITION	
SIGNATURE	

IN THE EVENT OF MY DEMISE I WANT THIS FIREARM TO GO TO	

NOTES

INFORMATION

BRAND		MODEL	
ACTION		GAUGE OR CALIBER	
BARREL		SIGHTS	
STOCKS OR GRIPS			
SERIAL #		CONDITION	
UNIQUE MARKS			

ACQUISITION DATE		COST		APPRAISED VALUE	

WHERE ACQUIRED	
COMMENTS	
HISTORY	
NOTES	

REPAIRS	DATE	COST

SOLD TO		
DATE		SELLING PRICE

ACQUISITION INFORMATION

PURCHASED FROM	
ADDRESS	
CONTACT NUMBER	

DATE		PRICE PAID	
ID NUMBER		D.O.B.	

CONDITION	
COMMENTS	

DISPOSITION INFORMATION

TRANSFER / SOLD TO	
ADDRESS	
CONTACT NUMBER	
FOID OR FFL #	

DATE		PRICE PAID	
ID NUMBER		D.O.B.	
LOST / STOLEN		INCIDENT #	

DETAILS	
CONDITION	
SIGNATURE	

IN THE EVENT OF MY DEMISE I WANT THIS FIREARM TO GO TO	

NOTES

INFORMATION

BRAND		MODEL	
ACTION		GAUGE OR CALIBER	
BARREL		SIGHTS	
STOCKS OR GRIPS			
SERIAL #		CONDITION	
UNIQUE MARKS			
ACQUISITION DATE		COST	APPRAISED VALUE
WHERE ACQUIRED			
COMMENTS			
HISTORY			
NOTES			

REPAIRS	DATE	COST

SOLD TO			
DATE		SELLING PRICE	

ACQUISITION INFORMATION

PURCHASED FROM	
ADDRESS	
CONTACT NUMBER	
DATE	PRICE PAID
ID NUMBER	D.O.B.
CONDITION	
COMMENTS	

DISPOSITION INFORMATION

TRANSFER / SOLD TO	
ADDRESS	
CONTACT NUMBER	
FOID OR FFL #	
DATE	PRICE PAID
ID NUMBER	D.O.B.
LOST / STOLEN	INCIDENT #
DETAILS	
CONDITION	
SIGNATURE	

IN THE EVENT OF MY DEMISE I WANT THIS FIREARM TO GO TO	

NOTES

INFORMATION

BRAND		MODEL	
ACTION		GAUGE OR CALIBER	
BARREL		SIGHTS	
STOCKS OR GRIPS			
SERIAL #		CONDITION	
UNIQUE MARKS			
ACQUISITION DATE		COST		APPRAISED VALUE	
WHERE ACQUIRED			
COMMENTS			
HISTORY			
NOTES			

REPAIRS	DATE	COST

SOLD TO	
DATE		SELLING PRICE	

ACQUISITION INFORMATION

PURCHASED FROM	
ADDRESS	
CONTACT NUMBER	
DATE	
ID NUMBER	
CONDITION	
COMMENTS	

DATE		PRICE PAID	
ID NUMBER		D.O.B.	

DISPOSITION INFORMATION

TRANSFER / SOLD TO	
ADDRESS	
CONTACT NUMBER	
FOID OR FFL #	
DATE	
ID NUMBER	
LOST / STOLEN	
DETAILS	
CONDITION	
SIGNATURE	

DATE		PRICE PAID	
ID NUMBER		D.O.B.	
LOST / STOLEN		INCIDENT #	

IN THE EVENT OF MY DEMISE I WANT THIS FIREARM TO GO TO	

NOTES

INFORMATION

BRAND		MODEL	
ACTION		GAUGE OR CALIBER	
BARREL		SIGHTS	
STOCKS OR GRIPS			
SERIAL #		CONDITION	
UNIQUE MARKS			

ACQUISITION DATE		COST		APPRAISED VALUE	

WHERE ACQUIRED	
COMMENTS	
HISTORY	
NOTES	

REPAIRS	DATE	COST

SOLD TO			
DATE		SELLING PRICE	

ACQUISITION INFORMATION

PURCHASED FROM	
ADDRESS	
CONTACT NUMBER	
DATE	PRICE PAID
ID NUMBER	D.O.B.
CONDITION	
COMMENTS	

DISPOSITION INFORMATION

TRANSFER / SOLD TO	
ADDRESS	
CONTACT NUMBER	
FOID OR FFL #	
DATE	PRICE PAID
ID NUMBER	D.O.B.
LOST / STOLEN	INCIDENT #
DETAILS	
CONDITION	
SIGNATURE	

IN THE EVENT OF MY DEMISE I WANT THIS FIREARM TO GO TO	

NOTES

INFORMATION

BRAND		MODEL	
ACTION		GAUGE OR CALIBER	
BARREL		SIGHTS	
STOCKS OR GRIPS			
SERIAL #		CONDITION	
UNIQUE MARKS			

ACQUISITION DATE		COST		APPRAISED VALUE	

WHERE ACQUIRED	
COMMENTS	
HISTORY	
NOTES	

REPAIRS	DATE	COST

SOLD TO		
DATE		SELLING PRICE	

ACQUISITION INFORMATION

PURCHASED FROM	
ADDRESS	
CONTACT NUMBER	
DATE	PRICE PAID
ID NUMBER	D.O.B.
CONDITION	
COMMENTS	

DISPOSITION INFORMATION

TRANSFER / SOLD TO	
ADDRESS	
CONTACT NUMBER	
FOID OR FFL #	
DATE	PRICE PAID
ID NUMBER	D.O.B.
LOST / STOLEN	INCIDENT #
DETAILS	
CONDITION	
SIGNATURE	

IN THE EVENT OF MY DEMISE I WANT THIS FIREARM TO GO TO	

NOTES

INFORMATION

BRAND		MODEL	
ACTION		GAUGE OR CALIBER	
BARREL		SIGHTS	
STOCKS OR GRIPS			
SERIAL #		CONDITION	
UNIQUE MARKS			

ACQUISITION DATE		COST		APPRAISED VALUE	

WHERE ACQUIRED	
COMMENTS	
HISTORY	
NOTES	

REPAIRS	DATE	COST

SOLD TO			
DATE		SELLING PRICE	

ACQUISITION INFORMATION

PURCHASED FROM	
ADDRESS	
CONTACT NUMBER	
DATE	PRICE PAID
ID NUMBER	D.O.B.
CONDITION	
COMMENTS	

DISPOSITION INFORMATION

TRANSFER / SOLD TO	
ADDRESS	
CONTACT NUMBER	
FOID OR FFL #	
DATE	PRICE PAID
ID NUMBER	D.O.B.
LOST / STOLEN	INCIDENT #
DETAILS	
CONDITION	
SIGNATURE	

IN THE EVENT OF MY DEMISE I WANT THIS FIREARM TO GO TO	

NOTES

INFORMATION

BRAND		MODEL	
ACTION		GAUGE OR CALIBER	
BARREL		SIGHTS	
STOCKS OR GRIPS			
SERIAL #		CONDITION	
UNIQUE MARKS			
ACQUISITION DATE		COST	APPRAISED VALUE
WHERE ACQUIRED			
COMMENTS			
HISTORY			
NOTES			

REPAIRS	DATE	COST

SOLD TO			
DATE		SELLING PRICE	

ACQUISITION INFORMATION

PURCHASED FROM	
ADDRESS	
CONTACT NUMBER	
DATE	PRICE PAID
ID NUMBER	D.O.B.
CONDITION	
COMMENTS	

DISPOSITION INFORMATION

TRANSFER / SOLD TO	
ADDRESS	
CONTACT NUMBER	
FOID OR FFL #	
DATE	PRICE PAID
ID NUMBER	D.O.B.
LOST / STOLEN	INCIDENT #
DETAILS	
CONDITION	
SIGNATURE	

IN THE EVENT OF MY DEMISE I WANT THIS FIREARM TO GO TO	

NOTES

INFORMATION

BRAND		MODEL	
ACTION		GAUGE OR CALIBER	
BARREL		SIGHTS	
STOCKS OR GRIPS			
SERIAL #		CONDITION	
UNIQUE MARKS			

ACQUISITION DATE		COST		APPRAISED VALUE	
WHERE ACQUIRED					
COMMENTS					
HISTORY					
NOTES					

REPAIRS	DATE	COST

SOLD TO	

DATE		SELLING PRICE	

ACQUISITION INFORMATION

PURCHASED FROM	
ADDRESS	
CONTACT NUMBER	
DATE	PRICE PAID
ID NUMBER	D.O.B.
CONDITION	
COMMENTS	

DISPOSITION INFORMATION

TRANSFER / SOLD TO	
ADDRESS	
CONTACT NUMBER	
FOID OR FFL #	
DATE	PRICE PAID
ID NUMBER	D.O.B.
LOST / STOLEN	INCIDENT #
DETAILS	
CONDITION	
SIGNATURE	

IN THE EVENT OF MY DEMISE I WANT THIS FIREARM TO GO TO	

NOTES

INFORMATION

BRAND		MODEL	
ACTION		GAUGE OR CALIBER	
BARREL		SIGHTS	
STOCKS OR GRIPS			
SERIAL #		CONDITION	
UNIQUE MARKS			

ACQUISITION DATE		COST		APPRAISED VALUE	

WHERE ACQUIRED	
COMMENTS	
HISTORY	
NOTES	

REPAIRS	DATE	COST

SOLD TO			
DATE		SELLING PRICE	

ACQUISITION INFORMATION

PURCHASED FROM	
ADDRESS	
CONTACT NUMBER	
DATE	PRICE PAID
ID NUMBER	D.O.B.
CONDITION	
COMMENTS	

DISPOSITION INFORMATION

TRANSFER / SOLD TO	
ADDRESS	
CONTACT NUMBER	
FOID OR FFL #	
DATE	PRICE PAID
ID NUMBER	D.O.B.
LOST / STOLEN	INCIDENT #
DETAILS	
CONDITION	
SIGNATURE	

IN THE EVENT OF MY DEMISE I WANT THIS FIREARM TO GO TO	

NOTES

INFORMATION

BRAND		MODEL	
ACTION		GAUGE OR CALIBER	
BARREL		SIGHTS	
STOCKS OR GRIPS			
SERIAL #		CONDITION	
UNIQUE MARKS			

ACQUISITION DATE		COST		APPRAISED VALUE	

WHERE ACQUIRED	
COMMENTS	
HISTORY	
NOTES	

REPAIRS	DATE	COST

SOLD TO			
DATE		SELLING PRICE	

ACQUISITION INFORMATION

PURCHASED FROM	
ADDRESS	
CONTACT NUMBER	
DATE	PRICE PAID
ID NUMBER	D.O.B.
CONDITION	
COMMENTS	

DISPOSITION INFORMATION

TRANSFER / SOLD TO	
ADDRESS	
CONTACT NUMBER	
FOID OR FFL #	
DATE	PRICE PAID
ID NUMBER	D.O.B.
LOST / STOLEN	INCIDENT #
DETAILS	
CONDITION	
SIGNATURE	

IN THE EVENT OF MY DEMISE I WANT THIS FIREARM TO GO TO	

NOTES

INFORMATION

BRAND		MODEL	
ACTION		GAUGE OR CALIBER	
BARREL		SIGHTS	
STOCKS OR GRIPS			
SERIAL #		CONDITION	
UNIQUE MARKS			
ACQUISITION DATE		COST	APPRAISED VALUE
WHERE ACQUIRED			
COMMENTS			
HISTORY			
NOTES			

REPAIRS	DATE	COST

SOLD TO			
DATE		SELLING PRICE	

ACQUISITION INFORMATION

PURCHASED FROM	
ADDRESS	
CONTACT NUMBER	
DATE	
ID NUMBER	
CONDITION	
COMMENTS	

Within the DATE / ID NUMBER rows: PRICE PAID, D.O.B.

DISPOSITION INFORMATION

TRANSFER / SOLD TO	
ADDRESS	
CONTACT NUMBER	
FOID OR FFL #	
DATE	
ID NUMBER	
LOST / STOLEN	
DETAILS	
CONDITION	
SIGNATURE	

Within the DATE / ID NUMBER / LOST-STOLEN rows: PRICE PAID, D.O.B., INCIDENT #

IN THE EVENT OF MY DEMISE I WANT THIS FIREARM TO GO TO	

NOTES

INFORMATION

BRAND		MODEL	
ACTION		GAUGE OR CALIBER	
BARREL		SIGHTS	
STOCKS OR GRIPS			
SERIAL #		CONDITION	
UNIQUE MARKS			

ACQUISITION DATE		COST	APPRAISED VALUE	
WHERE ACQUIRED				
COMMENTS				
HISTORY				
NOTES				

REPAIRS	DATE	COST

SOLD TO			
DATE		SELLING PRICE	

ACQUISITION INFORMATION

PURCHASED FROM	
ADDRESS	
CONTACT NUMBER	
DATE	PRICE PAID
ID NUMBER	D.O.B.
CONDITION	
COMMENTS	

DISPOSITION INFORMATION

TRANSFER / SOLD TO	
ADDRESS	
CONTACT NUMBER	
FOID OR FFL #	
DATE	PRICE PAID
ID NUMBER	D.O.B.
LOST / STOLEN	INCIDENT #
DETAILS	
CONDITION	
SIGNATURE	

IN THE EVENT OF MY DEMISE I WANT THIS FIREARM TO GO TO	

NOTES

INFORMATION

BRAND		MODEL	
ACTION		GAUGE OR CALIBER	
BARREL		SIGHTS	
STOCKS OR GRIPS			
SERIAL #		CONDITION	
UNIQUE MARKS			

ACQUISITION DATE		COST		APPRAISED VALUE	

WHERE ACQUIRED	
COMMENTS	
HISTORY	
NOTES	

REPAIRS	DATE	COST

SOLD TO		
DATE		SELLING PRICE

ACQUISITION INFORMATION

PURCHASED FROM			
ADDRESS			
CONTACT NUMBER			
DATE		PRICE PAID	
ID NUMBER		D.O.B.	
CONDITION			
COMMENTS			

DISPOSITION INFORMATION

TRANSFER / SOLD TO			
ADDRESS			
CONTACT NUMBER			
FOID OR FFL #			
DATE		PRICE PAID	
ID NUMBER		D.O.B.	
LOST / STOLEN		INCIDENT #	
DETAILS			
CONDITION			
SIGNATURE			

IN THE EVENT OF MY DEMISE I WANT THIS FIREARM TO GO TO	

NOTES

INFORMATION

BRAND		MODEL	
ACTION		GAUGE OR CALIBER	
BARREL		SIGHTS	
STOCKS OR GRIPS			
SERIAL #		CONDITION	
UNIQUE MARKS			

ACQUISITION DATE		COST		APPRAISED VALUE	

WHERE ACQUIRED	
COMMENTS	
HISTORY	
NOTES	

REPAIRS	DATE	COST

SOLD TO			
DATE		SELLING PRICE	

ACQUISITION INFORMATION

PURCHASED FROM	
ADDRESS	
CONTACT NUMBER	
DATE	PRICE PAID
ID NUMBER	D.O.B.
CONDITION	
COMMENTS	

DISPOSITION INFORMATION

TRANSFER / SOLD TO	
ADDRESS	
CONTACT NUMBER	
FOID OR FFL #	
DATE	PRICE PAID
ID NUMBER	D.O.B.
LOST / STOLEN	INCIDENT #
DETAILS	
CONDITION	
SIGNATURE	

IN THE EVENT OF MY DEMISE I WANT THIS FIREARM TO GO TO	

NOTES

INFORMATION

BRAND		MODEL	
ACTION		GAUGE OR CALIBER	
BARREL		SIGHTS	
STOCKS OR GRIPS			
SERIAL #		CONDITION	
UNIQUE MARKS			

ACQUISITION DATE		COST		APPRAISED VALUE	

WHERE ACQUIRED	
COMMENTS	
HISTORY	
NOTES	

REPAIRS	DATE	COST

SOLD TO			
DATE		SELLING PRICE	

ACQUISITION INFORMATION

PURCHASED FROM	
ADDRESS	
CONTACT NUMBER	

DATE		PRICE PAID	
ID NUMBER		D.O.B.	

CONDITION	
COMMENTS	

DISPOSITION INFORMATION

TRANSFER / SOLD TO	
ADDRESS	
CONTACT NUMBER	
FOID OR FFL #	

DATE		PRICE PAID	
ID NUMBER		D.O.B.	
LOST / STOLEN		INCIDENT #	

DETAILS	
CONDITION	
SIGNATURE	

IN THE EVENT OF MY DEMISE I WANT THIS FIREARM TO GO TO	

NOTES

INFORMATION

BRAND		MODEL	
ACTION		GAUGE OR CALIBER	
BARREL		SIGHTS	
STOCKS OR GRIPS			
SERIAL #		CONDITION	
UNIQUE MARKS			

ACQUISITION DATE		COST		APPRAISED VALUE	

WHERE ACQUIRED	
COMMENTS	
HISTORY	
NOTES	

REPAIRS	DATE	COST

SOLD TO	
DATE		SELLING PRICE	

ACQUISITION INFORMATION

PURCHASED FROM	
ADDRESS	
CONTACT NUMBER	
DATE	PRICE PAID
ID NUMBER	D.O.B.
CONDITION	
COMMENTS	

DISPOSITION INFORMATION

TRANSFER / SOLD TO	
ADDRESS	
CONTACT NUMBER	
FOID OR FFL #	
DATE	PRICE PAID
ID NUMBER	D.O.B.
LOST / STOLEN	INCIDENT #
DETAILS	
CONDITION	
SIGNATURE	

IN THE EVENT OF MY DEMISE I WANT THIS FIREARM TO GO TO	

NOTES

INFORMATION

BRAND		MODEL	
ACTION		GAUGE OR CALIBER	
BARREL		SIGHTS	
STOCKS OR GRIPS			
SERIAL #		CONDITION	
UNIQUE MARKS			

ACQUISITION DATE		COST		APPRAISED VALUE	

WHERE ACQUIRED	
COMMENTS	
HISTORY	
NOTES	

REPAIRS	DATE	COST

SOLD TO		
DATE		SELLING PRICE	

ACQUISITION INFORMATION

PURCHASED FROM	
ADDRESS	
CONTACT NUMBER	
DATE	PRICE PAID
ID NUMBER	D.O.B.
CONDITION	
COMMENTS	

DISPOSITION INFORMATION

TRANSFER / SOLD TO	
ADDRESS	
CONTACT NUMBER	
FOID OR FFL #	
DATE	PRICE PAID
ID NUMBER	D.O.B.
LOST / STOLEN	INCIDENT #
DETAILS	
CONDITION	
SIGNATURE	

IN THE EVENT OF MY DEMISE I WANT THIS FIREARM TO GO TO	

NOTES

INFORMATION

BRAND		MODEL	
ACTION		GAUGE OR CALIBER	
BARREL		SIGHTS	
STOCKS OR GRIPS			
SERIAL #		CONDITION	
UNIQUE MARKS			

ACQUISITION DATE		COST		APPRAISED VALUE	

WHERE ACQUIRED	
COMMENTS	
HISTORY	
NOTES	

REPAIRS	DATE	COST

SOLD TO			
DATE		SELLING PRICE	

ACQUISITION INFORMATION

PURCHASED FROM	
ADDRESS	
CONTACT NUMBER	
DATE	PRICE PAID
ID NUMBER	D.O.B.
CONDITION	
COMMENTS	

DISPOSITION INFORMATION

TRANSFER / SOLD TO	
ADDRESS	
CONTACT NUMBER	
FOID OR FFL #	
DATE	PRICE PAID
ID NUMBER	D.O.B.
LOST / STOLEN	INCIDENT #
DETAILS	
CONDITION	
SIGNATURE	

IN THE EVENT OF MY DEMISE I WANT THIS FIREARM TO GO TO	

NOTES

INFORMATION

BRAND		MODEL	
ACTION		GAUGE OR CALIBER	
BARREL		SIGHTS	
STOCKS OR GRIPS			
SERIAL #		CONDITION	
UNIQUE MARKS			
ACQUISITION DATE		COST	APPRAISED VALUE
WHERE ACQUIRED			
COMMENTS			
HISTORY			
NOTES			

REPAIRS	DATE	COST

SOLD TO		
DATE		SELLING PRICE

ACQUISITION INFORMATION

PURCHASED FROM	
ADDRESS	
CONTACT NUMBER	
DATE	PRICE PAID
ID NUMBER	D.O.B.
CONDITION	
COMMENTS	

DISPOSITION INFORMATION

TRANSFER / SOLD TO	
ADDRESS	
CONTACT NUMBER	
FOID OR FFL #	
DATE	PRICE PAID
ID NUMBER	D.O.B.
LOST / STOLEN	INCIDENT #
DETAILS	
CONDITION	
SIGNATURE	

IN THE EVENT OF MY DEMISE I WANT THIS FIREARM TO GO TO	

NOTES

INFORMATION

BRAND		MODEL	
ACTION		GAUGE OR CALIBER	
BARREL		SIGHTS	
STOCKS OR GRIPS			
SERIAL #		CONDITION	
UNIQUE MARKS			

ACQUISITION DATE		COST		APPRAISED VALUE	

WHERE ACQUIRED	
COMMENTS	
HISTORY	
NOTES	

REPAIRS	DATE	COST

SOLD TO			
DATE		SELLING PRICE	

ACQUISITION INFORMATION

PURCHASED FROM	
ADDRESS	
CONTACT NUMBER	
DATE	PRICE PAID
ID NUMBER	D.O.B.
CONDITION	
COMMENTS	

DISPOSITION INFORMATION

TRANSFER / SOLD TO	
ADDRESS	
CONTACT NUMBER	
FOID OR FFL #	
DATE	PRICE PAID
ID NUMBER	D.O.B.
LOST / STOLEN	INCIDENT #
DETAILS	
CONDITION	
SIGNATURE	

IN THE EVENT OF MY DEMISE I WANT THIS FIREARM TO GO TO	

NOTES

INFORMATION

BRAND		MODEL	
ACTION		GAUGE OR CALIBER	
BARREL		SIGHTS	
STOCKS OR GRIPS			
SERIAL #		CONDITION	
UNIQUE MARKS			

ACQUISITION DATE		COST		APPRAISED VALUE	

WHERE ACQUIRED	
COMMENTS	
HISTORY	
NOTES	

REPAIRS	DATE	COST

SOLD TO		
DATE		SELLING PRICE	

ACQUISITION INFORMATION

PURCHASED FROM	
ADDRESS	
CONTACT NUMBER	
DATE	
ID NUMBER	
CONDITION	
COMMENTS	

		PRICE PAID	
		D.O.B.	

DISPOSITION INFORMATION

TRANSFER / SOLD TO	
ADDRESS	
CONTACT NUMBER	
FOID OR FFL #	
DATE	
ID NUMBER	
LOST / STOLEN	
DETAILS	
CONDITION	
SIGNATURE	

		PRICE PAID	
		D.O.B.	
		INCIDENT #	

IN THE EVENT OF MY DEMISE I WANT THIS FIREARM TO GO TO	

NOTES

INFORMATION

BRAND		MODEL	
ACTION		GAUGE OR CALIBER	
BARREL		SIGHTS	
STOCKS OR GRIPS			
SERIAL #		CONDITION	
UNIQUE MARKS			

ACQUISITION DATE		COST		APPRAISED VALUE	

WHERE ACQUIRED	
COMMENTS	
HISTORY	
NOTES	

REPAIRS	DATE	COST

SOLD TO		
DATE		SELLING PRICE

ACQUISITION INFORMATION

PURCHASED FROM	
ADDRESS	
CONTACT NUMBER	
DATE	PRICE PAID
ID NUMBER	D.O.B.
CONDITION	
COMMENTS	

DISPOSITION INFORMATION

TRANSFER / SOLD TO	
ADDRESS	
CONTACT NUMBER	
FOID OR FFL #	
DATE	PRICE PAID
ID NUMBER	D.O.B.
LOST / STOLEN	INCIDENT #
DETAILS	
CONDITION	
SIGNATURE	

IN THE EVENT OF MY DEMISE I WANT THIS FIREARM TO GO TO	

NOTES

INFORMATION

BRAND		MODEL	
ACTION		GAUGE OR CALIBER	
BARREL		SIGHTS	
STOCKS OR GRIPS			
SERIAL #		CONDITION	
UNIQUE MARKS			

ACQUISITION DATE		COST		APPRAISED VALUE	
WHERE ACQUIRED					
COMMENTS					
HISTORY					
NOTES					

REPAIRS	DATE	COST

SOLD TO	
DATE		SELLING PRICE	

ACQUISITION INFORMATION

PURCHASED FROM	
ADDRESS	
CONTACT NUMBER	
DATE		PRICE PAID	
ID NUMBER		D.O.B.	
CONDITION	
COMMENTS	

DISPOSITION INFORMATION

TRANSFER / SOLD TO	
ADDRESS	
CONTACT NUMBER	
FOID OR FFL #	
DATE		PRICE PAID	
ID NUMBER		D.O.B.	
LOST / STOLEN		INCIDENT #	
DETAILS	
CONDITION	
SIGNATURE	

IN THE EVENT OF MY DEMISE I WANT THIS FIREARM TO GO TO	

NOTES

INFORMATION

BRAND		MODEL	
ACTION		GAUGE OR CALIBER	
BARREL		SIGHTS	
STOCKS OR GRIPS			
SERIAL #		CONDITION	
UNIQUE MARKS			

ACQUISITION DATE		COST		APPRAISED VALUE	

WHERE ACQUIRED	
COMMENTS	
HISTORY	
NOTES	

REPAIRS	DATE	COST

SOLD TO			
DATE		SELLING PRICE	

ACQUISITION INFORMATION

PURCHASED FROM	
ADDRESS	
CONTACT NUMBER	
DATE		PRICE PAID	
ID NUMBER		D.O.B.	
CONDITION	
COMMENTS	

DISPOSITION INFORMATION

TRANSFER / SOLD TO	
ADDRESS	
CONTACT NUMBER	
FOID OR FFL #	
DATE		PRICE PAID	
ID NUMBER		D.O.B.	
LOST / STOLEN		INCIDENT #	
DETAILS	
CONDITION	
SIGNATURE	

IN THE EVENT OF MY DEMISE I WANT THIS FIREARM TO GO TO	

NOTES

INFORMATION

BRAND		MODEL	
ACTION		GAUGE OR CALIBER	
BARREL		SIGHTS	
STOCKS OR GRIPS			
SERIAL #		CONDITION	
UNIQUE MARKS			

ACQUISITION DATE		COST		APPRAISED VALUE	

WHERE ACQUIRED	
COMMENTS	
HISTORY	
NOTES	

REPAIRS	DATE	COST

SOLD TO			
DATE		SELLING PRICE	

ACQUISITION INFORMATION

PURCHASED FROM	
ADDRESS	
CONTACT NUMBER	
DATE	PRICE PAID
ID NUMBER	D.O.B.
CONDITION	
COMMENTS	

DISPOSITION INFORMATION

TRANSFER / SOLD TO	
ADDRESS	
CONTACT NUMBER	
FOID OR FFL #	
DATE	PRICE PAID
ID NUMBER	D.O.B.
LOST / STOLEN	INCIDENT #
DETAILS	
CONDITION	
SIGNATURE	

IN THE EVENT OF MY DEMISE I WANT THIS FIREARM TO GO TO	

NOTES

Printed in the USA
CPSIA information can be obtained
at www.ICGtesting.com
LVHW081656141223
766523LV00018B/1133

9 781953 557490